Sea Things

A collection of poems by Carol Mead

Illustrated by Gareth Davies

Foreword

The sea runs through the veins of the British people: historically; economically and emotionally we are tied to it. Most of us live within a stone's throw of the coast so it is no surprise that culturally we have a powerful response to the waters around our island.

Carol and I grew up in coastal towns and, like many Brits, both of us owe our earliest childhood memories to the beach. Carol, however, was lucky enough to be raised on Ynys Môn (Isle of Anglesey) where there are all kinds of shorelines: sweeping sandy bays; quiet sheltered coves; tumultuous tidal rapids; and wave-battered rocky cliffs standing against the prevailing south westerly. As a marine biologist and conservationist based here I am still wide-eyed at the variety of habitats and marine life that occurs in such a small sea area. To a poet though, Ynys Môn must be a profound inspiration.

Carol spends most of her spare time exploring the coast (now with photo-artist husband, Glyn) and, like all the things in life that we come to know well, she cares a great deal about the sea. This deep-felt affection runs throughout Carol's writing in this book. Thankfully, her poetry is not 'high-brow'. Rather, it is accessible to a wide audience, young and old (eg *Me and Mr Shark*), and she captures how most of us feel about those early childhood memories. There is, however, more to Carol's work than the fun verses that my own children love to recite. Carol and I have chatted about many issues over the years such as the demise of fish stocks: we have a shared belief in the need for sustainably caught fish and proper marine reserves (www.mcsuk.org/). There has never been a time to be more concerned about our seas and Carol recognises this (eg *Fish 'n' Chips*).

Carol has spent a lifetime inspiring people to adopt fit, healthy and environmentally aware lifestyles – she is part of the coastal landscape. I have responded to this book more than to many of the cold, wet facts that science has offered me. At the end of the day, people make important decisions based on what touches them, and we conserve what we love, so I hope that the love of the sea in Carol's poems will inspire the rest of us care a little more about it.

Dr Bill Sanderson, 2009
Senior Marine Monitoring Ecologist
for a Welsh conservation agency

Contents

My Friends

Able Fitness – whether you walk the coastline, sail the seas, surf the waves or dive the depths, it is so important to be fit and healthy. Able Fitness offers private one-to-one training and individual fitness programmes to help you stay close to the sea!

1st Floor, Waverley House, Bridge Street, Menai Bridge, Anglesey LL59 5DN
Tel: 0776 4694297
Web: www.ablefitness.co.uk
E-mail: info@ablefitness.co.uk
Blog: www.angleseypersonaltrainer.blogspot.com

Ann's Pantry is a small cafe/restaurant near to the beach. We use local produce on our menus whenever possible and sustainability is very important to us. Enjoying wonderful sea views is part of life and work at Ann's Pantry.

Ann's Pantry, Moelfre, Anglesey LL72 8HH
Tel: 01248 410386
Web: www.annspantry.co.uk
E-mail: enquiries@annspantry.co.uk

Funsport is THE windsurfing, water sport and surf-wear shop in Rhosneigr (famous windsurfing and kite-surfing location). Run by sponsored sailors and instructors, Funsport is not just a shop for professional kit, it's a lifestyle – everything a surfer could need under one roof!

1 Beach Terrace, Rhosneigr, Anglesey LL64 5QB
Tel: 01407 810 899
Web: www.buckys.co.uk
E-mail: dave@buckys.co.uk
Open 9am - 5pm ALL year round

My Friends

The Oriel Glyn Davies Gallery
on Anglesey, houses hundreds of powerful
and dramatic seascape photographs by
eminent photo-artist and author,
Glyn Davies. The print editions are strictly
limited, on 200-year archival materials, signed
by the artist. Autographed coffee-table books
of Glyn's images are also available.

Bridge Street, Menai Bridge, Anglesey LL59 5DN
Tel: 01248 715511
Web: www.glyndavies.com
E-mail: glyn@glyndavies.com
Blog: www.anglesey-photo-artist.blogspot.com
Open: Tuesday to Saturday (ring for times)

Menai Oysters produces finest quality
oysters and mussels, from the fast-flowing
waters of the Menai Strait, Anglesey,
North Wales. The sea is integral to our
produce and gives our shellfish their
unique flavours.

Web: www.menaioysters.co.uk

Menai Oysters

Dewch i Gaernarfon am lyfrau Cymraeg
a Saesneg o Gymru a'r byd. Gwasanaeth
chwilota ac archebu penigamp.

Come to Caernarfon for books in English
and Welsh from bestsellers to unusual
finds. Personal and efficient search and
order service.

10 Stryd y Plas, Caernarfon
Gwynedd LL55 1RR
Tel: 01286 674631
Web: www.palasprint.com
E-mail: siop@palasprint.com

Illustrations

Gareth Davies was born on Anglesey in 1937. He trained at the Liverpool College of Art in Book Illustration and Printmaking from 1955 to 1959. At the end of this period he became the first ever winner of the John Moore's Scholarship for Graphics. At about this time he met his artist wife, Diana, a ceramicist and textile designer.

In 1961 he completed his one-year ATD course at Liverpool College of Art. He went on to teach in schools but in 1965 took up his post as Senior Lecturer in Printmaking at the Falmouth School of Art in Cornwall. He taught at the college until his retirement in 1987. Apart from commercial graphics, he continued with his own personal work, drawing and painting prolifically in his own studio throughout his teaching career.

In 1988 he returned to North Wales to live, and taught part-time in the Extra Mural Department of Bangor University. He continued to produce his own work using a wide range of mediums and these included mural paintings, set construction and technical drawings of vehicles for the Anglesey Transport Museum. He continues to produce personal drawings and exhibitions of his work in his homeland of North Wales.

2009

As far back as I can remember, I have enjoyed spending time at the seaside. During the summer, immediately after school each day, my mother would have a picnic ready, and armed with swimming costumes and towels we would catch the bus to the local beach. My mother was so good to us all, not only taking me and my sisters, but several of our friends too. When she met my stepfather, Pete, who had a car, we travelled to other beaches further afield. We had wonderful days out, which included ice creams and egg sandwiches, donkey rides, sandcastle building, rock pooling and playing in the sea.

When I was about ten years old we took our first family trip to Cornwall – MAGICAL! We stayed in a dilapidated caravan on a farm, and collected eggs and fresh milk from the farmer each morning. We spent our evenings on the beach, and sat eating fish and chips on harbour walls, watching the artists draw and paint on the quayside. We watched fishing boats come and go, usually throwing their catch out on to the sand. I remember seeing huge Skate lying next to the boats, plus other fascinating fish, which my mother proudly reeled off the names of!

When I had children of my own I was determined that they should have similar opportunities, memories and experiences. We spent hours on the beach, at every available opportunity, digging sandcastles, splashing in the sea, learning the names of shells, fish and rock pool creatures. We caught crabs, ate ice creams and had picnics. Later, my husband Glyn and I took my children for their first visit to Cornwall, for me a nostalgic trip, for Glyn a return to his roots but for all of us, a fantastic holiday. This has become an annual trip now, much loved and appreciated by all. We each have our favourite beach, campsites, ice cream flavours, pasty shops and clotted cream tea cafe.

Over the past few years I have learnt from marine biologist friends, such as Dr Bill Sanderson, that our fish stocks are in substantial decline, that even the most commonly known fish are endangered, that our seas are in trouble and that we ALL need to act now if we are to avoid a complete catastrophe. I can't bear the thought that the seaside is changing for the worse – I have loved being by the sea and enjoyed everything involved with the seaside, all my life. I want my children and their children to enjoy the same. In my own way, through writing poetry, hopefully accessible to all, I really hope to get the message across that not all is well in the marine world, which has comforted, amazed, pleasured and sustained us, in so many ways, across the generations.

This collection of poems celebrates the wonders of the sea, as well as highlighting some of the real concerns. Ultimately, I hope you will be as moved by some of these poems as you are delighted.

Carol Mead, 2009

Fish in the Sky

Birds in the sky
Fish in the sea
That is the way
it should be

But what would you say
if I said fish could fly?
Can you believe It?
Fish in the sky?

For I have seen them
Over the sea
Flapping their wings
And smiling at me

And even more crazy
And even more fun
I saw a small man
riding on one

You may see a fish
Smiling at you
And perhaps if you're lucky
You might just see two!

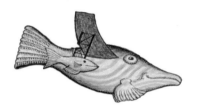

So when you go swimming
Don't look below
Take a look up
For you never know…

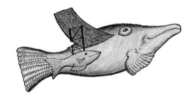

The stories are true
Fish really can fly!
Above the big sea
And so very high

But don't be surprised –
Show them you're brave.
Smile right back
And give them a

Great Big Wave!

In Search of the Sea

We went to the seaside
To swim and to splash,
To surf on the water
And watch the waves crash

But the sea had been stolen
Out of our hands,
No sign of water
Just miles of sand

So we set out to find
Where the ocean had gone,
We walked for a long time
We walked on and on

We splashed through some puddles
And looked for the sea,
With eyes on horizon
Where could it be?

Walking and walking
Our feet getting sore,
Walking and walking
To find the seashore

Then, at long last we found it
The ocean so blue,
Gigantic, enormous
A magnificent view

But then guess what happened?
It started to move,
The tide turning quickly
With something to prove

It chased us from shoreline
We ran very fast,
Water behind us
An ocean so vast

We raced back through puddles
We ran through the sand,
And finally made it
Back to dry land

The sea slowed behind us
The tide was full in,
At last we had time
To splash and to swim

A Busy Beach

The beach is full of tourists
And there's nowhere to sit down.
"It never used to be like this"
My Dad grumbles, with a frown

The sea is packed with bodies
Windbreakers everywhere.
"All these people on our beach"
Says Mum, "It really isn't fair"

We pick our way through sandcastles
Avoiding ocean spray.
"We should have stayed at home"
Says Dad
It is BANK HOLIDAY!"

People, people, everywhere
We can hardly see the sands!
Wetsuits, surfboards, tents and towels
All labelled with the latest brands!

A beach EXTREMELY busy
But we finally find a spot,
The tide high, so blue the sky
And the sun is VERY HOT!

At last we have a place to rest
A long way from the car,
My Dad is cross, my Mum complains,
"We had to walk so FAR"

But once we've had a cooling swim
Then sit to have a chatter,
Who really cares, how full the beach
We decide…
"It really doesn't matter!"

14

Our Seaside Picnic

Down at the seaside
My Dad and me –
Waiting for mum
To bring out the tea

Egg sarnies, ham sarnies
Biscuits and cheese –
Sausage rolls,
chocolate rolls
"don't forget to say please"

Here come the seagulls:
"Can you feed us?"
"Shoo" says my mother
"oh what a fuss"

"Go away seagulls
this is our tea,
we're having a picnic
Mum, Dad & me"

"Drink up your
orange juice –
Try not to spill"
"eat all your food"
"I promise, I will"

"Try not to drop any
Into the sand" –
"Oops there goes an apple
It dropped out of my hand!"

I love seaside picnics
But I have to eat fast –
Can't sit here too long
Time's whizzing past

For when we are finished,
My Dad and me
Mum tidies up
While we splash in the sea

Rock Pool Surprise!

We peer into rock pools
Holding buckets and nets,
Searching for creatures
We might like as pets

The water is clear
The seaweed is flowing,
"come out", "come out"
But nothing is showing

If we stay very still
and keep very calm,
"look, sea creatures moving,
Shhh, keep quiet, keep quiet
don't cause alarm"

▶

See the fish swimming,
And shrimps start to move,
"Two crabs are crawling
Look! Starfish!"
"Where?"
"There in the groove"

"Come by us, come by us"
As we stretch out our net,
But quickly they scatter
"You can't catch us yet!"

We'll wait a bit longer
Stand patient and still,
"They'll be back in a
moment, I promise,
they will"

"Yes, here they come now"
All swimming around,
"Fish, starfish, two crabs
And shrimps abound!"

18

"Now hold your net steady
And ready your arm,
Remember, remember,
Keep quiet and calm"

"Oh hurry, oh hurry
Lower it fast
Catch them, Catch them
Before they swim past"
"Oh too late, too late
I made such a fuss
But look over there
Aghh ….
a BIG octopus"

"Run quickly, run quickly
Over rocks and sand
Run quickly, run quickly
take my hand."
"Run quickly, run quickly
He may want us for tea!
Run quickly, run quickly
And follow me"

"STOP!"

"Why are we running?
What did he do?
Was he looking at me?
Or looking at you?
Shall we sneak back?
With bucket and net
Or is he too SCARY
To have as a pet?"

The Wibble Wobble Song

Wibble, Wobble, Wibble,
Wibble wobble-ish.
I am a strange
Glowing jellyfish

See me swimming slowly,
Wibble wobble-o.
In the current floating by
Going with the flow

Jelly, belly body,
Wibble wobble-ong.
Pulsating to the rhythm
Of the Wibble Wobble song

Wobble, wibble, wobble,
Wibble wobble-ide.
Let me brush against you
As I drift in with the tide

Feel my flowing tentacles,
Wobble wibble-oosh.
Sting and quickly disappear
With a Wibble Wobble

Me and Mr Shark

When I was in my boat today
A shark swam up to me.
"Jump," he said "into my mouth"
"I want you for my tea"

"Who, me you want?" I said to him,
"I think not Mr Shark."
"Inside my boat it's nice and light
Inside your mouth it's dark"

"Yes, dark" he said,
"but nice and warm
With lots of teeth to count."
"I could," I said "but count I can't
Not quite to that amount!"

He smiled at me
and showed his teeth
And oh yes there were many.
All white they were
and bright they were
As shiny as a penny

"Nice smile," I said to Mr Shark
"Good teeth and well looked after."
"Bad breath," I said,
"pooh what a smell"
This gave rise to his laughter

"You are funny"
He said to me
"I won't eat you today."
He turned his tail and waved at me
And then he swam away.

Song of the Blue Whale

I am a Blue Whale,
Big and strong.
Here is my story,
This is my song

I live in the ocean,
Which is very deep.
I eat as I swim
And I swim as I sleep

I am enormous,
Heavy and long.
And I use my huge tail
To push me along

I give birth to babies,
Just like you.
I have lungs to breathe,
I know you do too

24

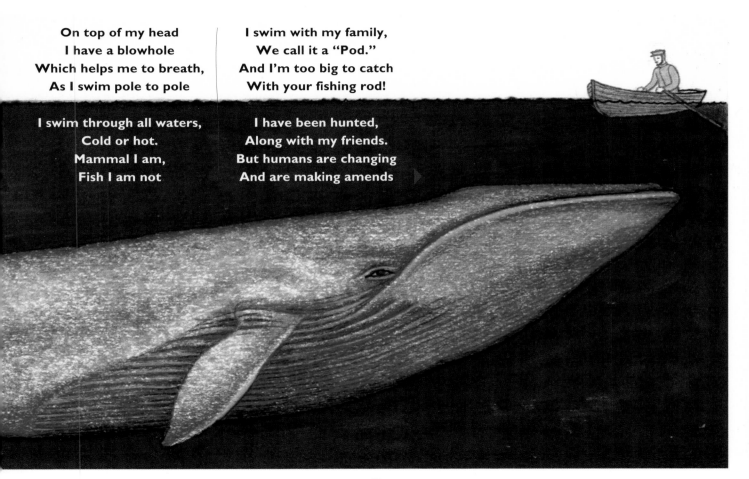

On top of my head
I have a blowhole
Which helps me to breath,
As I swim pole to pole

I swim with my family,
  We call it a "Pod."
And I'm too big to catch
With your fishing rod!

I swim through all waters,
  Cold or hot.
Mammal I am,
Fish I am not

I have been hunted,
Along with my friends.
But humans are changing
And are making amends

25

You hit us with harpoons
And caught us in nets.
But whales remember
One never forgets!

We've often been captured
NOT VERY NICE
It made us unhappy,
And made you think twice

About...

The way you treated us
Back in the past,
And now you regret it,
At last, at last

So let us keep swimming,
Deep in the sea.
To swim and survive,
We're alike you and me

I am a Blue Whale,
Big and strong.
Leave me alone
To sing my whale song

Singing my whale song,
Happy and free.
And if you are listening,
Please sing it with me.

Thank you.

An Enlightening Conversation

On my way to school today
I walked along the quay,
I stood to watch the fishermen
Prepare to put to sea

A local boat was setting sail
The Captain waved and smiled,
"Good day to take my vessel out" (he said)
"With sea so calm and mild"

"I don't catch cod or tuna" (he said)
"And I leave the skate alone,
I have no rods or trawling net
I leave them all at home"

I looked at him in disbelief
Then asked "why ever not?"
"No stock left" he said to me
"We've over-fished the lot"

"What's left need time to breed and grow,
It may be far too late" (he said)
I asked him to explain to me
He turned to the First Mate

"Ere Lad" (First Mate) "look over there
I'll tell you what we see,
Water, waves, the ebb and flow
And lots of vacant sea"

"Few fish there be" (he said)
"Near caught them all
to put them on our plate,
'Tis time to leave them well alone
To save them from their fate"

"So what do you do (I said)
When you are out
Upon the sea all day?"
I asked him to enlighten me
And wondered what he'd say

"We sit and talk and talk and sit
Play cards and drink a cuppa,
And when we feel the time is right
We head home for our supper" (he said)

And then they hauled the anchor up
And said "goodbye" to me,
I watched them motor out upon
An almost lifeless sea

Persistent Storm

I love to watch the ocean storms
Approach the harbour wall,
To witness tidal waves
Draw near
With endless rise and fall

The swell grows high
In energy,
Relentless as it thrashes,
The foaming water rushes in
Persistent as it crashes

With boom and splash and splash and boom
The noise is loud, yet hollow,
As each wave breaks with thunderous sound
Another one will follow

It travels far across the sea
And heads in my direction,
Then beats against this harbour wall
Which offers me protection

And as each storm beats on and on
Insistent, firm and strong,
I feel the power, the strength and force
A mighty ocean song

The Warning Light

Tall, majestic, solid, strong
Beam of light all night long.
Lighthouse stands against the storm
Blasting sound from its foghorn

Sailors heed the warning sound
Steer ships away from rocky ground.
From shallow water, swell and waves
To sail away from murky graves

If any night the squall blows through
Keepers know just what to do.
Flash the light to guide the way
Warning boats to keep away

The
Pompous Pirate

I am the Captain of my boat
A Pirate of the seas,
I answer to no King or Queen
And do just as I please

I sail the Caribbean Sea
And hide on islands green,
No army has yet captured me
I am a ghost unseen

I play chase with all naval ships
And fly my pirate's flag,
Through wind and rain and briny sea
A pirate's game of tag!

The skippers load their cannon balls
To blow my ship to bits,
But I will not surrender
"NO!"
A Pirate never quits

As broadside on our boats draw close
We stand and fight with vigour,
We always win, and celebrate
By drinking all their liquor

We gather up the swords and guns
It is a pirate duty,
We search the ship for coins and gold
And gather up our bootie

Then off we sail, my crew and I
To share our Pirate treasure,
A large percentage I acquire
To count out at my leisure

And if a pirate dares complain
I make him walk the plank,
Then write a note within my log
Of time and date he sank

I am the Captain of my boat
A mean and wicked crook,
Beware "me hearties" where you sail
And keep a watchful look

Look out for me upon the sea
I have no rule of thumb
Beware, beware I sing to thee
With a "Yo Ho Ho and a bottle of Rum!"

Me and the Boy

As I was swimming in the sea
I spied a boy and boat,
I swam to have a chat with him
And offer him my throat

He thought my offer quite absurd
And wasn't very keen,
I smiled and showed him all me teeth
He thought them very clean

He said that they were white and bright
But I couldn't understand,
Why he wouldn't jump into my mouth
And in my stomach land

He seemed to like it in his boat
Rather then my belly,
And as we talked about my tea
He said my breath was smelly!

How brave he was, this little boy
Who lightened up my day,
I told him that the meal was off
And wondered what he'd say

He didn't seem to think me weak
He didn't laugh or gloat,
So I turned my tail and swam away
And left him in his boat

Corky

We read about Corky
At an Internet site,
An Orca, majestic
Caught one winter's night.
From freedom to prison
Year upon year
It made us quite sad
And we each shed a tear.
She swims in a small tank
With four concrete walls
No family, no friends
Can hear her calls.
No ocean around her
No chance of release

For thirty-eight years
Not one day of peace.
Enclosed as a captive
Most times alone
Taken abruptly
From a place she called 'home'.
11th December
A day to recall
Others were captured
Seven in all
She has had her babies
But none have survived
A killer whale living
A free life denied

Creatures of the Deep

Deep in the darkness
On the sea floor
Imagine, imagine
Creatures galore

Possibly big
Possibly small
Some maybe swimming
While others may crawl

Down on the seabed
Life forms not seen
Gentle and kind ones
Or ferocious and mean

Create in your mind
A sea creature growing
With a head and a face
And a body that's glowing

Can they swim fast?
How would we know?
Deep in the darkness
Fathoms below

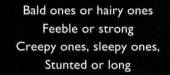

Bald ones or hairy ones
Feeble or strong
Creepy ones, sleepy ones,
Stunted or long

Round eyes or no eyes!
Legs or tails
Poisonous tentacles
With spikes or scales?

We know it is gloomy
As black as the night,
Where we picture them
Way out of sight?

Imagine, imagine
Creatures uncovered
Could they exist?
But not yet discovered!

Dolphin Appeal

Dolphin, Dolphin
Where are you?
The sun is shining
And the sky is blue.
Dolphin, Dolphin
Show me your fin
Jump out of the water
Then dive back in

Dolphin, Dolphin
Answer my call
I'm here alone
No one else here at all.
Dolphin, Dolphin
Just have a bash
To tumble turn
And make a BIG splash!

Dolphin, Dolphin
Hurry up please
Stop hiding from me
You're such a big tease.
Dolphin, Dolphin
Come out to play
Can you hear me calling
I want to see you today

Dolphin, Dolphin
At last you are here
With a smile on your face
I knew you could hear.
Dolphin, Dolphin
Swim closer to me
So I can watch you
And you can see me

I Want…

Today the wind is windy
Today the rain is wet.
I want to go out to the beach
"Not now," says Mum "Not yet"

I want to build a sandcastle
I want to build it high.
I want to build a sandcastle
That reaches to the sky

I want to dig a winding moat
Around my castle wall.
With turrets, towers and doorways
I want to build it all

I want to use my bucket
And fill the moat with sea.
"Daddy are you listening
Are you listening to me?"

I want to pour the water
Into the castle moat.
I want to fill it quickly
And float my plastic boat

I really want the wind to go away
I really want the rain to stop.
I really want to build my sandcastle
And stick a flag on top

But the weather is against me
And the sun will not come out.
So I'm standing at the window
As I stamp my feet and shout

I   want   you   to…

"LET ME OUT"

"please?"

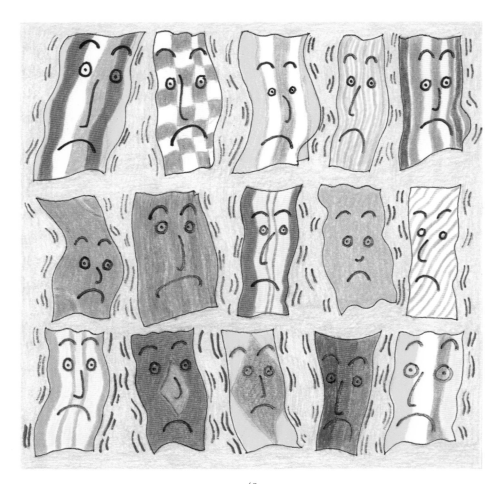

48

The Shiver, Shudder Experience

Shiver, Shudder
Freezing,
Shudder, shiver
Shake

Quiver judder
Goose bumps
Judder, quiver
Quake

Rattle prattle
Noisy teeth,
Chatter
Chattering

Had a swim,
Now I'm cold
Tremble
Trembling

Cosy comfy
Nice soft towel
Body warm
"Hooray!"

Rub me dry
No longer wet
And now I'm off
To play!

Sounds of the Seaside

Lie on the sand
And relax.
Feel the warmth of the sun
On your skin.
Listen to sounds,
All around,
hear the waves
Rolling in

Up above,
Gulls
Screeching and Calling

Then,
A new sound

Sand
Into a bucket falling

And

Far away, children play
And scream,
Perhaps demanding more Ice cream?

Then,
a lull

Broken by sound of
Ball against bat,
"smack"

Some people pass and chat,
Disturbing the world you have found,
Listening to sounds
All around

Then,
A pause

Chance to sleep

A lost cause

It's hard to reach,
As you lie
On a busy
Summer Beach

A Passion for Crabbing

I always love the seaside
I think it's rather fab,
I love to take my fishing net
To try and catch a crab

I love the way they move along
With eyes upon their head,
I'd like to catch a brown one
Or pink or maybe red!

They move along so quickly
Not forwards and not back,
But sidle to the left or right
As I follow in their track.

I see them clinging on to rocks
Deep down in a pool,
I wish I could catch one or two
To show them off at school!

Sometimes they try to pinch my toe
And squeeze it in a claw,
no matter how they torture me
I always look for more

When standing by the water's edge
When sitting in the sand,
I sometime see one sneaking by
and grab it in my hand,

And if I had one in my hand
As I caught it on the run,
My dad would laugh, my mum would scream
I'd think that such good fun!

Because,

I always love the seaside
With lots of things to do,
But catch a crab, I wish I could
"Have you caught one?"
"Have you?"

Starfish in a Pool

Little orange starfish
Underneath the sea.
In a rock pool catching food
Is where you like to be

Five small orange fingers, and little tubey feet.
Spiny, spiky body, and not too nice to eat!

Often called a Sea Star, changing shape to hide.
Crawl along the ocean floor, moving side to side

Little orange starfish
Underneath the sea.
Stay here in this rock pool
And be a friend to me

55

A Cornish Postcard

To Cornwall with our mum and dad
A family group of five,
We scrambled down the Logan rocks
To jump from them and dive.
We swam in water, shades of blue
And soaked up summer sun,
In Cornwall on our holiday
We had a lot of fun!

We climbed up cliffs, with ropes and gear
And snorkelled every day,
To Minack Theatre, Wednesday eve
To watch a Shakespeare play!
Devouring pasties for our lunch
Then scones and cream for tea,
We sailed a lugger boat, quite old,
Upon the Cornish sea

We braved the surf on body boards
On waves above head height,
Drank Mead in ancient Meaderies
Quite late into the night!
We watched the sun set in the west
From various golden sands,
Took photographs of granite stones
That makes up Cornish lands

We went to Cornwall for our hols
And have in years gone by,
We hate to leave and head for home
It always makes us cry.
From well-known towns and fishing bays
Sent postcards to our friends,
Watched dolphins in the sea at play
Where Cornwall's green land ends

As memories forever last,
And in our hearts remain,
The campsite booked for our return
To do it all again.
And when we enter parenthood,
And as our children grow,
As plans for holidays are made
To Cornwall we will go!

Sunset

We sit and watch the setting sun
Which marks the end of day.
The sky is bright
with red and gold
As daylight fades away

While evening falls
And shadows form
We hear a subtle hiss.
As ball of light
and sea ignite
When fire and ocean kiss

X

A Change of Season

In winter time
When the beach is empty
When the last of the tourists have gone.
We still visit the shore –
To paddle and walk and look for shells.
We run in and out of caves –
Looking for bears,
Then race out
screaming,
Only teasing.
Then fly our kite –
Simply having fun

In winter time
We still have a picnic or two
Tucked in amongst the rocks
sheltering from the wind and rain.
Our seaside food still tastes the same –
We drink hot, steaming, sugared tea
And huddle and cuddle under blanket or rugs
Just to keep warm.
While we watch
The winter waves form

In winter time
The seas are bigger,
The nights are longer
And the days are shorter.
But we still visit the shore
To see brave surfers catch a wave
So we can wave at them
And then
run off to kick or catch
our blue football.
And we talk as we walk
about
hot days and lazy days
That yet again
and once more
In another summertime
have gone

Fish 'n' Chips

Eating fish 'n' chips
Is a very British meal.
But when the fish have all been caught
How will it make us feel?

The cost of fish is rising
We think it quite unfair.
But when the fish have all been caught
There'll be none anywhere

Perhaps we should consider
The extinction we create?
As when the fish have all been caught
Regret will come too late

My Thanks

I would like to thank all the following people for their help and invaluable support:

Rich, Ed and Steph – my three fantastic children, who have listened intently to numerous readings of my draft poems and who, more importantly, have been the source of much inspiration for my work. My love for you all is, and always will be, deeper than any ocean. xxx

Leven Davies – my little nephew, who started the whole ball rolling with his love and enthusiasm for the first poem I sent him.

Gareth Davies – Lev's 'Taid' (grandfather) and my father-in-law, whose striking illustrations compliment my poems perfectly.

Glyn Davies – my incredible husband who constantly encourages, supports, believes in and loves me. Without this, my book would not be a reality! xx

Dr Bill Sanderson – Marine Biologist and a good friend, for such a wonderful foreword.

Jonathan Briggs – Designer, producer and good friend, who has not only put the book together from start to finish, but who has also provided astute business advice throughout!

My Friends – These companies have almost blindly given support to this book, but have made a huge contribution to its success. I can't thank them enough for their faith in a friend starting a new venture, so in short, thank you all, with total sincerity.